HAM RADIO

A Comprehensive Beginners Guide to Amateur Radio Operations, Equipment Setup and Licensing Process - Master the Fundamentals of Radio Communication with This Essential Handbook

Carl M. McShane

TABLE OF CONTENTS

Welcome to the world of ham radio, a realm where technology meets adventure and communication knows no bounds. In this introductory section, we'll embark on a journey through the captivating landscape of amateur radio, delving into its history, significance, and the endless possibilities it offers to enthusiasts worldwide.

Ham radio, also known as amateur radio, stands as a testament to human ingenuity and the enduring allure of wireless communication. It provides individuals with a unique platform to connect, experiment, and contribute to a global community bound by a shared passion for radio technology.

The roots of ham radio trace back to the pioneering efforts of early radio enthusiasts, whose experiments and innovations paved the way for the modern amateur radio community. From the groundbreaking discoveries of Marconi to the grassroots initiatives of amateur radio operators during times of crisis, the history of ham radio is rich with tales of innovation, resilience, and service.

In an age defined by instant communication and digital connectivity, one might question the relevance of amateur radio. However, the significance of ham radio extends far beyond mere communication; it serves as a lifeline during emergencies, a platform for technical exploration, and a medium for fostering friendships that transcend geographical boundaries.

As we journey deeper into the world of ham radio, we'll uncover the essential concepts, tools, and techniques that define this dynamic hobby. From understanding radio waves to mastering operating procedures, each aspect of amateur radio offers an opportunity for discovery, learning, and personal growth.

CHAPTER 1

OVERVIEW OF HAM RADIO

1.1 What is Ham Radio?

Ham radio, also known as amateur radio, is a unique hobby and service that allows individuals to communicate via radio waves using designated frequencies. Unlike commercial radio services, such as broadcast radio or cellular networks, ham radio operators have the freedom to experiment with various modes of communication, construct their own equipment, and engage in a wide range of activities, from local chatting to worldwide contests.

At its core, ham radio embodies the spirit of exploration and innovation, offering enthusiasts the opportunity to connect with like-minded individuals, contribute to emergency communication efforts, and explore the endless possibilities of radio technology. Whether it's making contacts with fellow operators across the globe, participating in public service events, or delving into the intricacies of radio propagation, ham radio provides a gateway to a world of adventure and discovery.

1.2 History of Amateur Radio

The history of amateur radio is a rich tapestry woven with the threads of innovation, experimentation, and the indomitable human spirit. It traces back to the late 19th century when pioneers like Guglielmo Marconi and Nikola Tesla made groundbreaking discoveries in wireless communication.

In 1894, Marconi achieved the first successful demonstration of wireless telegraphy, laying the foundation for what would become amateur radio. Throughout the early 20th century, radio enthusiasts, often referred to as "hams," began experimenting with radio waves, building their own equipment, and communicating with others over increasingly longer distances.

The Titanic disaster in 1912 highlighted the importance of wireless communication for maritime safety and spurred the development of regulations and licensing for amateur radio operators. In the following decades, amateur radio flourished as a hobby, with enthusiasts forming clubs, participating in contests, and advancing the technology through their innovative experiments.

During times of conflict, such as World War I and World War II, amateur radio operators played crucial roles in providing communication support and gathering intelligence. After World War II, the amateur radio community experienced a surge in popularity, as returning servicemen and civilians alike embraced the hobby as a means of personal expression and technical exploration.

Throughout the latter half of the 20th century and into the present day, amateur radio has continued to evolve, adapting to advancements in technology while preserving its rich heritage. Today, amateur radio enthusiasts span the globe, united by their passion for radio technology and their commitment to public service, experimentation, and lifelong learning. The history of amateur radio stands as a testament to the enduring spirit of discovery and community that defines this remarkable hobby.

1.3 Importance of Amateur Radio in Modern Communication

Amateur radio, often referred to as ham radio, holds a significant place in modern communication due to its versatility, resilience, and unique capabilities. Despite the proliferation of digital technologies, ham radio continues to play a vital role in various aspects of communication, including emergency response, technical innovation, and global connectivity.

1. Emergency Communication: One of the most critical roles of amateur radio is its contribution to emergency communication. During natural disasters, such as hurricanes, earthquakes, or floods, when traditional communication infrastructure may be compromised, ham radio operators step in to provide crucial communication links. Their ability to operate independently of centralized systems ensures that essential messages can be relayed, facilitating coordination among emergency responders and delivering vital information to affected communities.

2. Technical Innovation: Amateur radio serves as a fertile ground for technical experimentation and innovation. Enthusiasts are continually pushing the boundaries of radio technology, developing new modes of communication, building innovative equipment, and exploring emerging technologies such as software-defined radio and digital signal processing. These advancements not only benefit the amateur radio community but also contribute to broader technological developments in areas such as wireless networking and telecommunications.

3. Global Connectivity: Despite the prevalence of the internet and social media, ham radio offers a unique form of global connectivity. Through a network of repeaters, satellites, and digital modes, amateur radio operators can communicate with individuals across the street or around the world, fostering friendships and cultural exchange that transcend geographical boundaries. This global network of amateur radio enthusiasts serves as a testament to the power of communication to unite people from diverse backgrounds and cultures.

4. Community Service: Amateur radio operators are active participants in their communities, providing communication support for public events, such as marathons, parades, and festivals. They also volunteer their time and expertise to support public service organizations, including the Red Cross, Salvation Army, and local emergency management agencies. Through their dedication to service, ham radio operators demonstrate the positive impact that amateur radio can have on communities large and small.

In summary, the importance of amateur radio in modern communication cannot be overstated. Whether providing critical communication during emergencies, driving technical innovation, fostering global connectivity, or serving their communities, ham radio operators exemplify the enduring value of amateur radio in an increasingly connected world.

CHAPTER 2

2.1 Properties of Radio Waves

Radio waves are a form of electromagnetic radiation characterized by their ability to propagate through space without the need for a physical medium. Understanding the properties of radio waves is fundamental to comprehending how they are utilized in amateur radio communication. Here are some key properties:

1. Frequency: Radio waves are classified based on their frequency, which is measured in Hertz (Hz). Frequency determines the wave's behavior, including its ability to penetrate obstacles and travel long distances. Amateur radio operates across a wide range of frequencies, from very low frequencies (VLF) up to extremely high frequencies (EHF).

2. Wavelength: The wavelength of a radio wave is inversely proportional to its frequency, according to the equation: $\lambda = c / f$, where λ is the wavelength, c is the speed of light (approximately 3×10^8 meters per second), and f is the frequency. Longer wavelengths correspond to lower frequencies, while shorter wavelengths correspond to higher frequencies.

3. Propagation: Radio waves can propagate through various mediums, including air, water, and space. The manner in which they propagate depends on factors such as frequency, atmospheric conditions, and the presence of obstacles. Different propagation modes, such as ground wave, sky wave, and line-of-sight, determine the range and coverage of radio communication.

4. Polarization: Radio waves can be polarized horizontally, vertically, or circularly, depending on the orientation of the electric field relative to the Earth's surface. Polarization affects signal strength and reception quality, particularly in situations where signals are subject to reflection, scattering, or interference.

5. Attenuation: As radio waves travel through the atmosphere, they may experience attenuation, or weakening, due to absorption, scattering, and other factors. Higher frequencies are more susceptible to attenuation than lower frequencies, which is why certain frequency bands are better suited for long-distance communication or penetrating obstacles.

6. Propagation Effects: Various propagation phenomena, such as reflection, refraction, diffraction, and scattering, influence the behavior of radio waves in different environments. Understanding these effects is essential for predicting signal propagation, optimizing antenna performance, and maximizing communication range.

In summary, the properties of radio waves form the foundation of amateur radio communication, shaping the design of antennas, the selection of operating frequencies, and the prediction of propagation conditions. By mastering these properties, amateur radio operators can enhance their understanding of radio communication and maximize their effectiveness on the airwaves.

2.2 Frequency Bands and Allocation

Frequency bands in amateur radio refer to specific ranges of radio frequencies designated for amateur use by regulatory authorities such as the International Telecommunication Union (ITU) and national regulatory bodies like the Federal Communications

Commission (FCC) in the United States. Understanding frequency bands and their allocation is essential for amateur radio operators to operate within legal boundaries and efficiently utilize available spectrum. Here are the primary frequency bands allocated for amateur radio use:

1. Very Low Frequency (VLF):

Frequency Range: 3 kHz - 30 kHz

Description: VLF signals have long wavelengths and can penetrate seawater, making them suitable for submarine communication but impractical for most terrestrial amateur radio operations.

2. Low Frequency (LF):

Frequency Range: 30 kHz - 300 kHz

Description: LF signals propagate via ground wave, providing reliable communication over short to moderate distances. LF bands are used primarily for navigation aids, time signal broadcasts, and experimental purposes.

3. Medium Frequency (MF):

Frequency Range: 300 kHz - 3 MHz

Description: MF bands support both ground wave and sky wave propagation, offering reliable communication over moderate distances during the day and extended ranges via ionospheric reflection at night.

4. High Frequency (HF):

Frequency Range: 3 MHz - 30 MHz

Description: HF bands are widely utilized by amateur radio operators for long-distance communication via ionospheric propagation. HF bands are subdivided into multiple bands, each with unique propagation characteristics and usage preferences among operators.

5. Very High Frequency (VHF):

Frequency Range: 30 MHz - 300 MHz

Description: VHF bands enable line-of-sight communication over relatively short distances, typically within a few hundred kilometers. VHF bands are commonly used for local and regional communication, including FM repeater operation, satellite communication, and amateur television.

Ultra High Frequency (UHF):

Frequency Range: 300 MHz - 3 GHz

Description: UHF bands support line-of-sight communication similar to VHF but with shorter wavelengths and higher frequencies. UHF bands are utilized for various purposes in amateur radio, including simplex and repeater operation, satellite communication, and data transmission.

7. Microwave Bands:

Frequency Range: Above 1 GHz (1,000 MHz)

Description: Microwave bands encompass frequencies above 1 GHz and are characterized by their short wavelengths and high data-carrying capacities. Microwave bands are utilized for point-to-point communication, experimentation, and amateur television.

These frequency bands are allocated globally, but specific allocations may vary by country or region. Amateur radio operators must adhere to band plans and frequency allocations established by their respective regulatory authorities to ensure orderly and efficient use of the radio spectrum. By understanding frequency bands and their allocation, amateur radio operators can navigate the airwaves effectively and participate in diverse modes of communication within the amateur radio community.

2.3 Propagation Characteristics

Understanding propagation characteristics is essential for amateur radio operators to predict how radio waves will travel from the transmitter to the receiver. Various factors influence propagation, including frequency, time of day, solar activity, terrain, and atmospheric conditions. Here are some key propagation characteristics relevant to amateur radio:

1. Ground Wave Propagation:

Description: Ground wave propagation occurs when radio waves travel along the surface of the Earth, following the curvature of the Earth. It is predominant in the low frequency (LF) and medium frequency (MF) bands.

Distance: Ground wave propagation is effective for short to moderate distances, typically up to a few hundred kilometers, depending on frequency and terrain.

2. Sky Wave Propagation:

Description: Sky wave propagation involves the reflection of radio waves off the ionosphere, allowing them to travel long distances over the horizon. It is most prevalent in the high frequency (HF) bands.

Distance: Sky wave propagation enables communication over thousands of kilometers, especially during periods of high solar activity and at night when the ionosphere is more ionized.

3. Ionospheric Layers:

Description: The Earth's ionosphere consists of several layers of charged particles that can reflect, refract, or absorb radio waves. The main layers relevant to amateur radio are the D layer, E layer, F1 layer, and F2 layer.

Effect on Propagation: Each ionospheric layer interacts differently with radio waves based on frequency, angle of incidence, and time of day, influencing signal propagation and characteristics such as skip distance and signal strength.

4. Skip Distance:

Description: Skip distance refers to the distance between the transmitter and the point where the sky wave returns to Earth. It varies based on frequency, angle of radiation, and ionospheric conditions.

Effect on Communication: Understanding skip distance helps operators determine the optimal frequency and antenna orientation for communicating with distant stations via sky wave propagation.

5. Fading and Multipath Propagation:

Description: Fading occurs when radio signals fluctuate in strength due to changes in propagation conditions, such as ionospheric variations or signal reflection. Multipath propagation involves the reception of multiple signal paths due to reflection, diffraction, or scattering.

Effect on Reception: Fading and multipath propagation can cause fluctuations in signal strength, distortion, and interference, affecting the quality of communication.

6. Tropospheric Propagation:

Description: Tropospheric propagation involves the bending of radio waves in the lower atmosphere due to temperature inversions, atmospheric ducting, or weather conditions.

Effect on Communication: Tropospheric propagation can enhance VHF and UHF communication over long distances, allowing signals to travel beyond the line-of-sight horizon under certain atmospheric conditions.

By understanding these propagation characteristics, amateur radio operators can anticipate and adapt to changing propagation conditions, optimize their station setup, and maximize their effectiveness in communicating with other operators around the world.

CHAPTER 3

ESSENTIAL COMPONENTS OF A HAM RADIO STATION

3.1 Transceivers: The Heart of the Station

Transceivers, short for transmitter-receiver, serve as the central component of any amateur radio station, facilitating both transmission and reception of radio signals. As the cornerstone of communication, transceivers come in various forms and designs, offering a wide range of features and capabilities to suit the diverse needs of amateur radio operators. Here's an overview of transceivers and their essential characteristics:

1. Functionality: Transceivers integrate the functions of both a transmitter and a receiver into a single device, allowing operators to transmit and receive radio signals on designated frequencies. They enable two-way communication, enabling operators to engage in real-time conversations with other stations.

2. Frequency Coverage: Transceivers are designed to operate across specific frequency bands allocated for amateur radio use. Depending on the model, transceivers may cover one or multiple frequency bands, ranging from HF (high frequency) to VHF (very high frequency) and UHF (ultra high frequency). Wideband transceivers may also support additional frequency ranges for general coverage reception.

3. Modes of Operation: Transceivers support various modes of operation, including amplitude modulation (AM), frequency modulation (FM), single sideband (SSB), and digital modes such as Morse code (CW) and digital data transmission. They may also incorporate advanced digital signal processing (DSP) capabilities for enhanced performance and signal filtering.

4. Power Output: Transceivers are rated by their power output, which determines the strength of the transmitted signal. Power output typically ranges from a few watts to several hundred watts, depending on the transceiver's design and intended use. Higher power transceivers are capable of reaching greater distances and overcoming propagation challenges.

5. Controls and Interface: Transceivers feature a user-friendly interface with controls for adjusting frequency, mode, power level, and other parameters.

They may incorporate a combination of knobs, buttons, and digital displays for intuitive operation. Advanced transceivers may also offer customizable settings, programmable memory channels, and built-in signal processing tools.

6. Connectivity: Transceivers provide various connectivity options for external devices, including antennas, microphones, headphones, and computer interfaces. They may feature multiple antenna connectors for different bands, as well as ports for data communication and accessory connections.

7. Size and Portability: Transceivers come in a range of sizes and form factors, from compact handheld models suitable for portable operation to desktop units designed for base station use. Portable transceivers often feature built-in batteries, rugged construction, and lightweight designs for outdoor activities and emergency communication.

8. Accessories and Expansion: Transceivers can be customized and expanded with a wide range of accessories, including external antennas, amplifiers, tuners, filters, and digital interfaces. These accessories enhance performance, expand operating capabilities, and tailor the transceiver to specific operating preferences and requirements.

Transceivers are the heart of every amateur radio station, providing the essential means to communicate with other operators and explore the fascinating world of radio communication. Whether for casual conversations, emergency communication, or competitive contests, selecting the right transceiver is key to unlocking the full potential of amateur radio operation.

3.2 Antennas: Gateway to the Airwaves

Antennas are the critical link between your amateur radio transceiver and the vast expanse of the airwaves. As the primary radiating element of your station, antennas play a pivotal role in transmitting and receiving radio signals efficiently. Understanding the characteristics and principles of antennas is essential for optimizing your station's performance and maximizing your ability to communicate effectively. Let's explore the world of antennas and their significance in amateur radio operation:

1. Functionality: Antennas are devices designed to convert electrical signals into electromagnetic waves for transmission and to capture incoming electromagnetic waves for reception. They serve as the interface between your transceiver and the surrounding electromagnetic environment, enabling communication over radio frequencies.

2. Radiation Patterns: Antennas exhibit specific radiation patterns that describe how electromagnetic energy is distributed in space. Common radiation patterns include omnidirectional, which radiates energy equally in all directions, and directional, which concentrates energy in specific directions. Understanding the radiation pattern of an antenna is crucial for directing signals towards desired locations or avoiding interference from unwanted directions.

3. Frequency Coverage: Antennas are designed to operate within specific frequency ranges, corresponding to the amateur radio bands allocated by regulatory authorities. Different antennas are optimized for different frequency bands, with some antennas capable of covering multiple bands through tunable or multiband designs. Matching the antenna's frequency range to the desired operating frequencies is essential for efficient signal transmission and reception.

4. Types of Antennas:

There is a wide variety of antenna types, each offering unique characteristics and performance attributes. Common antenna types used in amateur radio include:

a. Dipole Antennas: Simple and efficient antennas consisting of two conductive elements connected to the transmission line.

b. Vertical Antennas: Antennas designed for ground-mounted or elevated operation, providing omnidirectional or directional radiation patterns.

c. Yagi-Uda Antennas: Directional antennas composed of multiple elements arranged in a specific configuration to achieve high gain and directivity.

d. Loop Antennas: Compact antennas formed into loops or coils, offering excellent performance for portable and space-constrained installations.

e. Wire Antennas: Versatile antennas constructed from wire elements, such as longwire, end-fed, or wire dipole antennas, suitable for a wide range of frequencies and applications.

5. Installation Considerations: Proper installation and placement of antennas are crucial for optimal performance and efficiency. Factors to consider include antenna height, orientation, polarization, grounding, and clearance from nearby objects. Careful planning and experimentation may be necessary to achieve the desired coverage, minimize interference, and comply with local regulations.

6. Matching Networks and Tuners: Some antennas require impedance matching networks or tuners to ensure efficient power transfer between the antenna and the transceiver. These devices adjust the antenna's impedance to match the impedance of the transmission line, maximizing power transfer and minimizing standing wave ratio (SWR) for improved performance.

7. Maintenance and Care: Regular maintenance and inspection are essential to ensure the continued reliability and performance of your antennas. Periodically check for signs of corrosion, damage, or deterioration, and clean the antenna elements and connections as needed. Properly securing and weatherproofing outdoor antennas can help prevent damage from environmental factors and ensure long-term durability.

In summary, antennas are the gateway to the airwaves, serving as the essential link between your amateur radio station and the world beyond. By understanding the principles of antenna design, selecting the appropriate antenna type for your operating needs, and ensuring proper installation and maintenance, you can unleash the full potential of your station and embark on exciting communication adventures across the amateur radio bands.

3.3 Power Supplies and Accessories

In the realm of amateur radio, power supplies and accessories are the unsung heroes that ensure seamless operation, provide essential functionality, and enhance the overall user experience. From supplying reliable power to your transceiver to augmenting your station with additional capabilities, understanding the role of power supplies and accessories is crucial for optimizing your amateur radio setup. Let's delve into the world of power supplies and accessories and explore their significance in amateur radio operation:

1. Power Supplies: Power supplies are vital components that provide the electrical energy necessary to operate your amateur radio equipment. They convert alternating current (AC) from mains power sources or direct current (DC) from batteries or solar panels into stable DC power suitable for powering transceivers, amplifiers, and other station accessories. When selecting a power supply for your amateur radio station, consider factors such as output voltage and current capacity, efficiency, noise level, and reliability to ensure compatibility with your equipment and operational requirements.

2. Batteries and Backup Power: Batteries serve as indispensable backup power sources for amateur radio stations, providing resilience in the event of mains power outages or portable operations away from conventional power sources. Common battery types used in amateur radio include lead-acid batteries, nickel-metal hydride (NiMH) batteries, lithium-ion batteries, and sealed lead-acid (SLA) batteries. Consider factors such as capacity, voltage, weight, and rechargeability when selecting batteries for your station's backup power needs.

3. Antenna Tuners: Antenna tuners, also known as antenna matching units or transmatches, are accessories that optimize the match between your transceiver and antenna system, ensuring efficient power transfer and minimizing standing wave ratio (SWR). They adjust the impedance of the antenna system to match the impedance of the transmission line, allowing maximum power to be delivered to the antenna and reducing the risk of damage to the transceiver. Antenna tuners are particularly useful for multiband antennas or antennas with non-resonant frequencies.

4. Filters and Signal Processors: Filters and signal processors are accessories designed to enhance the quality of transmitted and received signals by filtering out unwanted noise, interference, and spurious emissions. They come in various forms, including band-pass filters, noise filters, audio filters, and digital signal processing (DSP) units. Filters and signal processors help improve signal clarity, reduce fatigue during extended operating sessions, and mitigate the effects of atmospheric noise and electromagnetic interference.

5. SWR Meters and Test Equipment: SWR (standing wave ratio) meters and other test equipment are essential accessories for monitoring and troubleshooting your amateur radio station's performance. SWR meters measure the impedance match between your transceiver and antenna system, allowing you to adjust antenna tuners or antenna lengths for optimal performance. Other test equipment, such as power meters, oscilloscopes, and spectrum analyzers, provide valuable insights into signal characteristics, performance metrics, and RF behavior, enabling informed decision-making and diagnostic capabilities.

6. Remote Control and Station Automation: Remote control and station automation accessories empower amateur radio operators to operate their stations remotely, monitor operating parameters, and automate routine tasks. Remote control interfaces, software-defined radio (SDR) systems, and networked control systems enable operators to access their stations from anywhere with an internet connection, allowing for flexible operating arrangements, remote contests, and unattended operation during emergencies.

7. Accessories for Portable and Mobile Operations: For portable and mobile amateur radio operations, specialized accessories such as portable antennas, compact power supplies, lightweight mast systems, and portable shelter solutions are essential for setting up temporary stations in the field. These accessories enable operators to participate in outdoor activities, emergency communication exercises, and DXpeditions while maintaining flexibility, mobility, and self-sufficiency.

In summary, power supplies and accessories play indispensable roles in amateur radio operation, providing essential functionality, enhancing performance, and enabling a wide range of operating scenarios. By selecting high-quality equipment, understanding their capabilities, and integrating them effectively into your station setup, you can enhance your amateur radio experience and unlock new possibilities for communication, experimentation, and exploration across the amateur radio bands.

3.4 Operating Modes: CW, SSB, FM, Digital, and More

Operating modes in amateur radio refer to the methods and techniques used to modulate and demodulate radio signals for communication purposes. Each operating mode has its unique characteristics, advantages, and applications, catering to diverse interests and preferences within the amateur radio community. Let's explore some of the most common operating modes utilized by amateur radio operators:

1. Continuous Wave (CW): CW, also known as Morse code, is one of the oldest and most enduring operating modes in amateur radio. It involves the transmission of on-off keying signals, where a continuous wave carrier is interrupted to create Morse code characters. CW is valued for its simplicity, efficiency, and ability to achieve long-distance communication under challenging conditions, making it popular among DXers, contesters, and enthusiasts of traditional operating methods.

2. Single Sideband (SSB): SSB is a voice communication mode widely used on HF (high frequency) bands in amateur radio. It involves the transmission of only one sideband of the modulated signal, resulting in reduced bandwidth and increased efficiency compared to full-carrier AM (amplitude modulation). SSB offers excellent voice quality and is favored for long-distance communication due to its ability to overcome noise and interference.

3. Frequency Modulation (FM): FM is a voice communication mode commonly used on VHF (very high frequency) and UHF (ultra high frequency) bands in amateur radio. It modulates the carrier frequency by varying its frequency in response to the audio signal. FM provides high-fidelity voice transmission and is well-suited for local communication, repeater operation, and mobile or handheld transceivers.

4. Digital Modes: Digital modes utilize digital signal processing techniques to encode and decode information transmitted over radio waves. They offer advantages such as robustness against noise and interference, efficient bandwidth utilization, and error correction capabilities. Common digital modes used in amateur radio include:

a. PSK31 (Phase Shift Keying 31)

b. RTTY (Radio Teletype)

c. FT8 (Franke-Taylor design, 8-FSK)

d. JT65 (Joe Taylor, 65-tone)

e. APRS (Automatic Packet Reporting System)

f. Packet Radio

g. Amplitude Modulation (AM):

AM is a voice communication mode that modulates the carrier amplitude in proportion to the audio signal. While less common in amateur radio than SSB and FM, AM offers a nostalgic appeal and is used by some operators for local communication, vintage equipment operation, and AM broadcasting experiments.

5. Other Specialty Modes: In addition to the standard operating modes mentioned above, amateur radio enthusiasts may experiment with various specialty modes and techniques, including:

a. Slow Scan Television (SSTV)

b. Moonbounce (EME)

c. Meteor Scatter

d. Satellite Communication

e. Digital Voice Modes (D-STAR, System Fusion, DMR)

f. Weak Signal Modes (JT9, FT4, WSPR)

Each operating mode offers its unique challenges, rewards, and opportunities for exploration within the amateur radio hobby. Whether pursuing DX contacts, participating in contests, experimenting with digital communication, or simply enjoying casual conversations, amateur radio operators have a wealth of operating modes at their disposal to suit their interests and operating preferences.

CHAPTER 4

4.1 License Classes and Privileges

In amateur radio, license classes define the levels of proficiency and privileges granted to operators by regulatory authorities. Obtaining a license is a crucial step for participating in amateur radio activities, allowing operators to access specific frequency bands and modes of operation. License classes vary from country to country, but they generally consist of multiple tiers, each offering progressively more privileges and responsibilities. Let's explore the typical license classes and their associated privileges:

1. Technician Class:

Entry-level license granting basic operating privileges on VHF (very high frequency) and UHF (ultra high frequency) bands.

Privileges typically include voice and digital communication on frequencies above 50 MHz, as well as limited privileges on HF bands.

Technician-class operators can communicate using FM (frequency modulation) repeaters, participate in local nets, and engage in satellite communication.

2. General Class:

Intermediate-level license providing expanded operating privileges on HF bands in addition to VHF and UHF privileges.

Privileges include voice and digital communication on HF bands, enabling long-distance communication both domestically and internationally.

General-class operators can access a wider range of frequencies, modes, and operating privileges, including access to HF contesting, DX (long-distance) communication, and digital modes.

3. Extra Class:

Highest level of amateur radio license, offering the most extensive privileges and operating freedoms.

Privileges include access to all amateur radio frequency bands, including exclusive allocations on HF bands, as well as additional privileges on VHF, UHF, and microwave bands.

Extra-class operators have access to the entire spectrum of amateur radio activities, including high-power operation, experimental modes, and participation in prestigious contests and awards programs.

4. Additional Privileges:

In addition to class-specific privileges, amateur radio operators may obtain additional privileges through specialized endorsements, certifications, or operating awards. These may include:

a. Morse code (CW) proficiency endorsements

b. Satellite communication endorsements

c. Radiotelegraph operator certificates

d. VHF/UHF contesting awards

e. DXCC (DX Century Club) awards for contacting stations in numerous countries

f. Special operating privileges for emergency communication and public service activities

5. Licensing Requirements:

Licensing requirements for each class vary by country and regulatory authority but generally include passing written examinations covering technical theory, operating procedures, and regulations. In some countries, practical assessments or Morse code proficiency tests may be required for certain license classes.

6. Upgrade Paths:

Amateur radio operators often progress through the license classes by upgrading their licenses through additional examinations and study. Each license class builds upon the privileges of the previous class, providing a pathway for operators to expand their knowledge, skills, and operating capabilities over time.

By obtaining amateur radio licenses and progressing through the license classes, operators gain access to a wide range of privileges and opportunities for exploration and experimentation within the vibrant amateur radio community. Whether pursuing local communication, DX contacts, contesting, or emergency communication, amateur radio offers a rewarding and fulfilling hobby for operators of all skill levels.

Preparing for an amateur radio license exam requires diligence, study, and familiarity with the relevant technical concepts, regulations, and operating procedures. Fortunately, numerous resources and study materials are available to assist aspiring amateur radio operators in their exam preparation journey. Here's a comprehensive guide to exam preparation resources:

1. Study Guides and Manuals:

Obtain official study guides and manuals published by amateur radio organizations or licensing authorities. These guides cover the exam syllabus comprehensively and provide explanations, examples, and practice questions to aid in understanding.

Look for study guides tailored to specific license classes (e.g., Technician, General, Extra) to focus your preparation on the relevant exam content.

2. Online Courses and Webinars:

Enroll in online courses or webinars offered by amateur radio clubs, organizations, or educational platforms. These courses provide structured learning modules, video lectures, and interactive quizzes to reinforce learning and retention.

Many online courses offer flexibility in scheduling and pacing, allowing you to study at your own pace and review challenging topics as needed.

3. Practice Exams and Mock Tests:

Take advantage of practice exams and mock tests available online or through amateur radio study apps. These simulated exams mimic the format and content of the actual licensing exams, allowing you to assess your knowledge, identify areas of weakness, and track your progress over time.

Practice exams are invaluable for familiarizing yourself with the exam structure, time constraints, and question types, helping to build confidence and reduce test anxiety.

4. Amateur Radio Clubs and Elmers:

Join local amateur radio clubs or seek guidance from experienced operators known as "Elmers." These mentors can provide invaluable advice, practical tips, and hands-on assistance in exam preparation.

Amateur radio clubs often offer study groups, licensing classes, and informal gatherings where members can exchange knowledge, share resources, and collaborate on exam preparation.

5. Online Forums and Communities:

Participate in online forums, discussion groups, and social media communities dedicated to amateur radio. These platforms provide opportunities to ask questions, seek advice, and engage with fellow operators who have firsthand experience with exam preparation and licensing.

Share your progress, seek recommendations for study materials, and connect with others preparing for the same exams to benefit from collective knowledge and support.

6. Textbooks and Reference Materials:

Consult textbooks, reference manuals, and technical publications covering topics relevant to amateur radio licensing exams. These resources offer in-depth explanations, diagrams, and real-world examples to supplement your understanding of key concepts.

Look for textbooks recommended by licensing authorities or amateur radio organizations, as they are likely to align closely with exam syllabi and requirements.

7. Online Study Tools and Apps:

Explore online study tools and mobile apps designed specifically for amateur radio exam preparation. These tools often include flashcards, quizzes, reference materials, and interactive tutorials to reinforce learning and retention.

Choose apps that offer customizable study plans, progress tracking features, and offline access for convenient studying anytime, anywhere.

8. Self-paced Learning and Review:

Establish a regular study routine and dedicate sufficient time each day or week to exam preparation. Break down the exam syllabus into manageable topics and prioritize areas where you need additional review or practice.

Use a variety of study methods, including reading, listening to lectures, watching instructional videos, and hands-on experimentation with amateur radio equipment, to reinforce learning and cater to different learning styles.

By leveraging these exam preparation resources and incorporating a disciplined study approach, you can increase your chances of success on amateur radio licensing exams and embark on your journey as a licensed amateur radio operator with confidence and proficiency.

4.3 FCC Regulations and Compliance

Understanding Federal Communications Commission (FCC) regulations is essential for amateur radio operators to ensure lawful and responsible operation within the amateur radio service. The FCC establishes rules and guidelines governing amateur radio operation to promote safety, spectrum efficiency, and adherence to international agreements. Here's an overview of key FCC regulations and compliance requirements for amateur radio operators:

1. Licensing Requirements:

Amateur radio operators must obtain an FCC-issued amateur radio license to legally transmit on amateur radio frequencies. Different license classes (e.g., Technician, General, Extra) grant varying privileges and operating frequencies.

Licensees must renew their licenses periodically and comply with any license renewal or administrative requirements specified by the FCC.

2. Frequency Allocations:

The FCC allocates specific frequency bands for amateur radio use, ranging from low frequencies (LF) to microwave frequencies (microwaves). Amateur radio operators must operate within these allocated frequency bands and adhere to band plans established by national amateur radio organizations.

Operators must also comply with frequency band restrictions, such as avoiding unauthorized transmissions on restricted bands or frequencies reserved for other radio services.

3. Emission Types and Power Limits:

The FCC specifies permissible emission types (e.g., CW, SSB, FM, digital modes) and power limits for amateur radio transmissions. Operators must use emission types and power levels consistent with their license class and the rules governing their operating privileges.

Unauthorized modifications to equipment, excessive power output, and deliberate interference are prohibited and may result in FCC enforcement actions or license revocation.

4. Station Identification:

Amateur radio stations must transmit their assigned call signs at specific intervals and at the beginning and end of each communication session. Call signs serve as unique identifiers for each station and are used to track and regulate amateur radio activity.

Operators must adhere to FCC regulations regarding the format, timing, and frequency of call sign transmissions to ensure accurate identification and compliance with licensing requirements.

5. Interference and Operation Considerations:

Amateur radio operators are responsible for minimizing interference to other radio services and complying with FCC regulations regarding interference mitigation. This includes avoiding harmful interference to primary users, such as government agencies and commercial broadcasters, and resolving interference complaints promptly and cooperatively.

Operators must also exercise caution when operating near sensitive frequencies or in proximity to emergency communications, military installations, and aviation frequencies.

6. Emergency Communications and Public Service:

Amateur radio operators play a vital role in providing emergency communication support during disasters, public emergencies, and community events. The FCC encourages amateur radio operators to participate in public service activities and emergency preparedness drills, provided they comply with licensing requirements and coordination protocols.

Operators must prioritize emergency traffic, maintain situational awareness, and cooperate with emergency responders and public safety agencies during emergency operations.

7. RF Exposure and Safety:

The FCC sets limits on radio frequency (RF) exposure to protect individuals from potential health hazards associated with RF radiation. Amateur radio operators must ensure compliance with RF exposure limits when installing, operating, and maintaining transmitting equipment.

Operators should follow best practices for RF safety, such as maintaining safe distances from antennas, using appropriate shielding and grounding techniques, and posting warning signs in areas where RF exposure may exceed permissible limits.

By familiarizing themselves with FCC regulations and adhering to compliance requirements, amateur radio operators can enjoy the privileges of amateur radio operation while promoting responsible and lawful use of the radio spectrum. Staying informed about regulatory updates, participating in amateur radio organizations, and seeking guidance from experienced operators can help ensure ongoing compliance and safe, enjoyable amateur radio experiences.

CHAPTER 5

5.1 Choosing the Right Equipment

Selecting the appropriate amateur radio equipment is a crucial decision that significantly impacts your operating experience, capabilities, and enjoyment of the hobby. Whether you're a newly licensed operator or a seasoned veteran, choosing the right equipment requires careful consideration of your operating preferences, budget, technical requirements, and future aspirations. Here's a comprehensive guide to help you navigate the process of selecting the right equipment for your amateur radio station:

1. Define Your Operating Goals:

Clarify your primary objectives and interests in amateur radio, such as DXing, contesting, emergency communication, digital modes, satellite communication, or experimenting with new technologies. Your operating goals will influence the type of equipment best suited to your needs.

2. Assess Frequency and Mode Requirements:

Determine the frequency bands and operating modes you plan to utilize based on your license class, operating privileges, and preferred activities. Consider whether you require equipment capable of HF, VHF, UHF, or microwave operation, as well as specific modes such as CW, SSB, FM, or digital modes.

3. Consider Your Operating Environment:

Evaluate the physical space available for your amateur radio station, including indoor or outdoor installations, antenna restrictions, and portability requirements. Choose equipment that fits your space constraints and environmental conditions, whether for home, mobile, or portable operation.

4. Budget and Affordability:

Establish a realistic budget for purchasing amateur radio equipment, taking into account the cost of transceivers, antennas, accessories, and any ancillary equipment required for your station setup. Balance affordability with performance and quality to ensure value for your investment.

5. Research Equipment Options:

Research available equipment options from reputable manufacturers and vendors, including transceivers, antennas, amplifiers, tuners, power supplies, and accessories. Read product reviews, user testimonials, and technical specifications to compare features, performance, and reliability.

6. Seek Recommendations and Advice:

Seek recommendations and advice from experienced amateur radio operators, club members, Elmers, and online forums. Gather insights into recommended equipment choices, potential pitfalls, and tips for optimizing your station setup based on real-world experiences and expertise.

7. Consider Used and Refurbished Equipment:

Explore the option of purchasing used or refurbished equipment to maximize your budget and access higher-end gear at lower costs. Be cautious when buying used equipment, and verify its condition, functionality, and warranty coverage before making a purchase.

8. Test Equipment Before Purchase:

Whenever possible, test amateur radio equipment before making a purchase to evaluate its performance, usability, and compatibility with your operating preferences. Attend ham radio conventions, swap meets, or equipment demonstrations to experience different models firsthand.

9. Plan for Future Expansion:

Anticipate your future needs and aspirations in amateur radio, and choose equipment that offers room for growth and expansion. Look for equipment with upgradeable features, modular designs, and compatibility with future accessories or enhancements.

10. Prioritize Quality, Reliability, and Support:

Prioritize equipment quality, reliability, and after-sales support when making purchasing decisions. Invest in reputable brands known for their craftsmanship, customer service, and long-term reliability to minimize downtime and maximize your enjoyment of the hobby.

By following these guidelines and conducting thorough research, you can confidently choose the right amateur radio equipment that aligns with your operating goals, budget, and technical requirements. Remember that selecting equipment is a personal decision, and there's no one-size-fits-all solution—choose equipment that suits your individual preferences and operating style to ensure a fulfilling and rewarding amateur radio experience.

5.2 Antenna Installation and Tuning

Installing and tuning your antenna is a critical step in setting up an effective amateur radio station. Proper installation and tuning ensure efficient transmission and reception of radio signals, maximizing your station's performance and communication capabilities. Here's a step-by-step guide to antenna installation and tuning:

1. Selecting the Antenna:

Choose an antenna type suitable for your operating goals, frequency bands, and installation environment. Consider factors such as antenna gain, radiation pattern, polarization, and space constraints when selecting the antenna.

2. Site Survey and Planning:

Conduct a site survey to identify suitable locations for antenna installation, considering factors such as height, clearance, grounding, and proximity to obstructions. Choose a location that minimizes signal blockage, maximizes line-of-sight visibility, and complies with local regulations.

3. Mounting the Antenna:

Install the antenna securely using appropriate mounting hardware and techniques. Ensure that the antenna is mounted at the desired height and orientation for optimal performance, taking into account factors such as antenna radiation pattern and directional characteristics.

4. Connecting Feedline and Grounding:

Connect the feedline (coaxial cable) from the antenna to your transceiver or antenna tuner using suitable connectors and cable routing techniques. Implement proper grounding measures to protect against static discharge, lightning strikes, and RF interference.

5. Antenna Tuning and Matching:

Use an antenna tuner or matching network to adjust the impedance of the antenna system to match the impedance of the transmission line. Tune the antenna tuner to achieve a low standing wave ratio (SWR) and maximum power transfer between the transceiver and antenna.

6. SWR Measurement and Adjustment:

Measure the standing wave ratio (SWR) of the antenna system using an SWR meter or built-in SWR measurement feature on your transceiver. Adjust the antenna tuner or antenna length to minimize SWR and achieve resonance at the desired operating frequency.

7. Testing and Fine-Tuning:

Conduct on-air tests and signal checks to verify the performance of the antenna system. Make adjustments as needed to optimize antenna placement, orientation, and tuning for improved signal strength, clarity, and reliability.

8. Maintenance and Inspection:

Regularly inspect the antenna system for signs of damage, corrosion, or wear. Clean the antenna elements, connectors, and feedline periodically to ensure reliable operation and minimize signal loss.

9. Documentation and Record-Keeping:

Maintain detailed documentation of your antenna installation, including antenna specifications, mounting configuration, tuning adjustments, and SWR measurements. Keep records of maintenance activities, repairs, and upgrades to track the performance and history of your antenna system.

10. Compliance with Regulations:

Ensure that your antenna installation complies with relevant regulations, zoning ordinances, and homeowners' association (HOA) rules governing antenna height, placement, and aesthetics. Obtain necessary permits or approvals if required by local authorities.

By following these steps and best practices, you can install and tune your amateur radio antenna system effectively, ensuring optimal performance and reliable communication capabilities for your amateur radio station. Remember to consult antenna manuals, manufacturer recommendations, and experienced operators for additional guidance and troubleshooting assistance as needed.

5.3 Grounding and Lightning Protection

Grounding and lightning protection are crucial aspects of amateur radio station installation, ensuring safety, equipment protection, and reliable operation in the event of electrical storms or power surges. Proper grounding techniques and lightning protection measures mitigate the risk of damage to equipment and minimize the potential for injury to operators. Here's a comprehensive guide to grounding and lightning protection for amateur radio stations:

1. Establish a Grounding System:

Install a robust grounding system for your amateur radio station, consisting of ground rods, grounding conductors, and grounding busbars or panels. Ensure that all metallic components, such as antennas, feedlines, towers, and equipment enclosures, are bonded to the grounding system to provide a common reference point for electrical safety and lightning protection.

2. Bonding and Bonding Conductors:

Bond all metallic components of your amateur radio station together using bonding conductors or straps made of copper or other suitable materials. Bonding minimizes potential differences and reduces the risk of equipment damage from transient currents and lightning-induced voltages.

3. Grounding for Antennas and Towers:

Ground antennas and towers using multiple ground rods spaced at intervals around the perimeter of the installation. Connect the ground rods to the tower base and antenna mounting hardware using heavy-gauge grounding conductors to ensure effective grounding and lightning dissipation.

4. Surge Protection Devices:

Install surge protection devices, such as gas discharge tubes (GDTs), transient voltage suppressors (TVSs), or metal-oxide varistors (MOVs), at key points in your amateur radio station's electrical system. Surge protectors divert excess voltage and transient currents away from sensitive equipment, preventing damage from power surges and lightning strikes.

5. Coaxial Cable Grounding:

Ground coaxial cables at their entry points into the station using surge protectors or bulkhead grounding connectors. Bond the outer conductor (shield) of the coaxial cable to the grounding system to provide a low-impedance path for lightning-induced currents and static discharge.

6. Lightning Arrestors and Spark Gaps:

Install lightning arrestors or spark gaps in series with antenna feedlines to shunt high-voltage surges and lightning strikes to ground. Lightning arrestors provide a path of least resistance for lightning-induced currents, protecting equipment and minimizing the risk of damage.

7. Equipotential Bonding:

Implement equipotential bonding to equalize electrical potentials between metallic objects within the station, including equipment racks, antennas, mast structures, and utility entrances. Equipotential bonding reduces the risk of electrical shock and minimizes damage from lightning-induced arcing and sparking.

8. Grounding and Lightning Protection Plan:

Develop a comprehensive grounding and lightning protection plan for your amateur radio station, outlining procedures for installation, maintenance, and periodic inspections. Train operators and personnel on safety protocols and emergency procedures in the event of electrical storms or lightning activity.

9. Periodic Inspections and Maintenance:

Regularly inspect the grounding system, lightning protection devices, and surge suppressors for signs of corrosion, damage, or degradation. Perform maintenance tasks, such as cleaning connections, tightening bolts, and replacing worn components, to ensure the integrity and effectiveness of the grounding and lightning protection system.

10. Compliance with Regulations:

Ensure that your grounding and lightning protection measures comply with relevant electrical codes, standards, and regulations governing amateur radio installations. Consult local building codes, NEC (National Electrical Code) requirements, and industry best practices to ensure compliance and safety.

By implementing proper grounding and lightning protection measures, amateur radio operators can safeguard their equipment, protect against electrical hazards, and maintain reliable communication capabilities even in the face of adverse weather conditions and electrical disturbances. Prioritize safety and compliance when designing and installing your station's grounding and lightning protection system to ensure a secure and resilient operating environment for amateur radio operation.

CHAPTER 6

BASIC OPERATING PROCEDURES

6.1 Calling CQ and Making Contacts

Calling CQ and making contacts is the essence of amateur radio operation, allowing operators to connect with fellow enthusiasts around the world and engage in diverse communication activities. Whether you're a newcomer to the hobby or an experienced operator, mastering the art of calling CQ and making successful contacts enhances your enjoyment and participation in amateur radio. Here's a step-by-step guide to calling CQ and making contacts:

1. Prepare Your Station:

Ensure that your amateur radio station is set up and ready for operation. Power on your transceiver, tune to a clear frequency within your licensed privileges, and verify that your antenna system is properly tuned and optimized for the desired frequency band.

2. Choose a Frequency and Band:

Select an appropriate frequency and band based on propagation conditions, time of day, and your operating preferences. Refer to band plans, propagation forecasts, and DX spotting networks to identify active frequencies and potential DX (long-distance) opportunities.

3. Listen Before Transmitting:

Before calling CQ, listen carefully to the frequency to check for ongoing conversations, net operations, or other activity. Use your transceiver's receiver to scan for signals, adjust the frequency or mode as needed, and ensure that you're operating within an available portion of the band.

4. Craft Your CQ Call:

Formulate a concise and clear CQ call that includes your call sign, location, and any additional information relevant to your operating preferences or objectives. Keep your CQ call brief but informative, allowing other operators to quickly identify and respond to your transmission.

5. Transmit Your CQ Call:

Key your microphone or activate your keying device to transmit your CQ call. Speak clearly and enunciate your call sign and location, maintaining proper spacing and timing between transmissions. Monitor the frequency for responses while transmitting your CQ call to listen for potential contacts.

6. Listen for Responses:

After transmitting your CQ call, release your transmission and listen attentively for responses from other amateur radio operators. Use your transceiver's receiver to scan for incoming signals, paying attention to signal strength, clarity, and call signs of potential contacts.

7. Respond to Incoming Calls:

If you receive a response to your CQ call or hear other operators calling CQ, respond promptly with your call sign and a signal report. Acknowledge the station you're contacting, exchange any relevant information, and engage in friendly conversation or exchange of operating details.

8. Confirm the Contact:

Once you've established communication with another station, confirm the contact by exchanging call signs, signal reports, and any other pertinent information required for logging purposes. Note the time, frequency, mode, and details of the contact in your logbook for future reference.

9. QSO Etiquette and Courtesy:

Practice good operating etiquette and courtesy during your contacts, respecting frequency usage, avoiding unnecessary interference, and adhering to established operating practices. Listen actively, wait for breaks in conversation, and take turns transmitting to maintain a smooth and orderly exchange.

10. Expand Your Horizons:

Explore different operating modes, bands, and communication techniques to broaden your amateur radio experience and reach new contacts worldwide. Participate in contests, special events, and DXpeditions to challenge yourself, sharpen your skills, and connect with fellow enthusiasts across the globe.

By following these steps and incorporating best practices into your operating routine, you can effectively call CQ and make successful contacts in the amateur radio community. Remember to approach each contact with enthusiasm, curiosity, and a spirit of camaraderie, fostering connections and friendships that enrich your amateur radio journey.

6.2 Using Q Codes and Ham Jargon

Q codes and ham jargon are essential elements of amateur radio communication, providing concise and standardized codes, abbreviations, and terminology to convey information efficiently and effectively during on-air conversations. Mastering Q codes and ham jargon enhances your ability to communicate clearly, expedite exchanges, and participate in diverse amateur radio activities. Here's a guide to using Q codes and ham jargon in amateur radio communication:

1. Understand the Purpose of Q Codes:

Q codes originated from the early days of Morse code telegraphy and were later adapted for voice communication in amateur radio. Q codes serve as shorthand for common phrases, questions, and requests, enabling operators to convey information quickly and succinctly during on-air exchanges.

2. Learn Common Q Codes:

Familiarize yourself with commonly used Q codes relevant to amateur radio operations. Examples include:

QSL: "I acknowledge receipt" or "I confirm"

QSO: "Conversation" or "Contact"

QTH: "Location"

QRP: "Reduced power"

QRZ: "Who is calling me?"

QRT: "Stop transmitting" or "Signing off"

QSY: "Change frequency"

QRM: "Interference" or "Man-made noise"

QRN: "Atmospheric noise" or "Natural interference"

3. Use Q Codes Appropriately:

Incorporate Q codes into your on-air conversations when appropriate, using them to pose questions, respond to inquiries, confirm details, or signal your intentions. Avoid overusing Q codes or using them in contexts where plain language may be more suitable.

4. Decode Q Codes from Others:

Listen actively to other operators using Q codes during on-air exchanges, and decode their meanings based on context and familiarity with common Q code definitions. Pay attention to how Q codes are used in different situations and adapt your responses accordingly.

5. Expand Your Ham Jargon Vocabulary:

Expand your repertoire of ham jargon and operating terminology beyond Q codes to include common phrases, abbreviations, and slang used in amateur radio conversations. Examples include:

"CQ": Calling any station

"73": Best regards

"DX": Distant station or long-distance contact

"YL" and "OM": Young lady and Old man (referring to female and male operators, respectively)

"RST": Readability, signal strength, and tone (used to report signal quality)

"73s" and "88s": Best regards and love, respectively (used in closing statements)

"Ham shack": Amateur radio station or operating location

"Elmer": Experienced operator who mentors or guides newcomers in the hobby

6. Adapt to Regional Variations:

Be aware that ham jargon and operating practices may vary regionally or among different amateur radio communities. Adapt to local customs and preferences when communicating with operators from diverse backgrounds or geographical areas.

7. Practice Clear Communication:

Strive for clarity and precision in your on-air communication, using plain language, proper pronunciation, and clear enunciation to ensure that your messages are easily understood by other operators. Avoid excessive abbreviations or jargon that may be unfamiliar to some listeners.

8. Respect Operating Etiquette:

Use Q codes and ham jargon in a manner that respects established operating etiquette and norms within the amateur radio community. Be courteous, patient, and cooperative during on-air exchanges, and adhere to accepted practices for frequency usage, calling procedures, and signal reporting.

9. Seek Guidance and Feedback:

Seek guidance from experienced operators, club members, or online resources to expand your understanding of Q codes, ham jargon, and operating practices. Ask questions, seek clarification on unfamiliar terms, and solicit feedback on your on-air communication skills to improve over time.

10. Enjoy the Experience:

Embrace the rich tradition and camaraderie of amateur radio communication, and have fun exploring the diverse world of Q codes, ham jargon, and on-air conversations. Celebrate the unique language and culture of amateur radio while forging meaningful connections with fellow enthusiasts worldwide.

By incorporating Q codes and ham jargon into your amateur radio communication repertoire and adopting best practices for clear and courteous on-air exchanges, you can enhance your operating experience, facilitate smooth communication, and foster connections with operators around the globe.

6.3 Conducting Proper Station Etiquette

Maintaining proper station etiquette is essential for fostering positive interactions, promoting effective communication, and upholding the integrity of the amateur radio community. Whether you're making contacts, participating in nets, or engaging in on-air conversations, adhering to established etiquette guidelines ensures a respectful and enjoyable experience for all operators involved. Here's a comprehensive guide to conducting proper station etiquette in amateur radio:

1. Listen Before Transmitting:

Before transmitting, listen attentively to the frequency to ensure it's not already in use. Respect ongoing conversations, net operations, and established protocols, and wait for an appropriate opportunity to join the conversation or call CQ.

2. Identify Yourself Clearly:

Clearly identify yourself using your call sign at the beginning and end of each transmission, as required by licensing regulations. Enunciate your call sign slowly and phonetically to ensure accurate identification, especially during challenging propagation conditions.

3. Follow Calling Procedures:

Adhere to established calling procedures when initiating contacts or calling CQ. Use standard calling frequencies, announce your intention to make a contact, and wait for responses before proceeding with the exchange. Avoid monopolizing frequencies or engaging in extended transmissions without allowing others to join the conversation.

4. Respect Frequency Usage:

Respect frequency allocations, band plans, and operating guidelines established by national amateur radio organizations and regulatory authorities. Avoid operating on frequencies designated for specific modes, activities, or emergency communications without proper authorization or coordination.

5. Maintain Clear Communications:

Speak clearly and concisely when transmitting voice communications, using proper modulation and volume levels to ensure that your signals are easily understood by other operators. Enunciate words, avoid mumbling or speaking too quickly, and minimize background noise or distractions.

6. Practice Active Listening:

Listen actively to other operators during on-air exchanges, paying attention to their call signs, signal reports, and operating preferences. Give each operator the opportunity to speak, avoid interrupting or talking over others, and wait for breaks in conversation to interject or respond.

7. Provide Clear Signal Reports:

Provide accurate and meaningful signal reports when exchanging signal reports with other operators. Use standard signal report formats, such as RST (Readability, Signal Strength, Tone), to convey signal quality and reception conditions accurately.

8. Be Courteous and Respectful:

Treat fellow operators with courtesy, respect, and professionalism at all times. Avoid contentious topics, inflammatory language, or disruptive behavior that may detract from the enjoyment of others. Foster a welcoming and inclusive atmosphere that encourages participation and camaraderie among operators.

9. Exercise Patience and Tolerance:

Exercise patience and tolerance when communicating with operators of varying experience levels, backgrounds, and operating styles. Be understanding of language barriers, technical limitations, and cultural differences, and offer assistance or guidance to newcomers as needed.

10. Resolve Disputes Amicably:

Handle disputes or conflicts with other operators diplomatically and constructively, seeking resolution through respectful dialogue and compromise. Avoid escalating conflicts or engaging in confrontational behavior that may disrupt on-air activities or harm the reputation of amateur radio as a whole.

11. Promote Safety and Compliance:

Prioritize safety, compliance, and adherence to regulatory requirements in all aspects of amateur radio operation. Follow established safety protocols, equipment guidelines, and licensing regulations to ensure a secure and lawful operating environment for yourself and others.

12. Lead by Example:

Lead by example and set a positive tone for on-air interactions by demonstrating exemplary station etiquette, professionalism, and goodwill toward fellow operators. Encourage others to follow suit and uphold the highest standards of conduct and integrity in amateur radio communication.

By following these guidelines and embodying the principles of proper station etiquette, amateur radio operators can contribute to a vibrant, respectful, and harmonious operating environment that fosters camaraderie, learning, and mutual respect among operators worldwide. Letting etiquette guide your interactions ensures that everyone can enjoy the hobby to its fullest potential.

CHAPTER 7

EMERGENCY COMMUNICATION AND PUBLIC SERVICE

7.1 Role of Amateur Radio in Emergencies

Amateur radio, often referred to as "ham radio," plays a crucial role in emergency communication, providing a reliable and resilient means of communication when traditional channels are disrupted or overloaded during disasters, crises, or public emergencies. Amateur radio operators, equipped with their knowledge, skills, and specialized equipment, serve as vital links in emergency response efforts, facilitating communication, coordination, and assistance to affected communities. Here's an overview of the role of amateur radio in emergencies:

1. Emergency Communication Networks:

Amateur radio operators form a resilient network of communicators capable of maintaining communication links when conventional infrastructure, such as landline telephony, cellular networks, or the internet, becomes unavailable or impaired during emergencies.

2. Redundant Communication Channels:

Amateur radio provides redundant communication channels that complement existing emergency communication systems, offering backup capabilities to public safety agencies, emergency responders, and humanitarian organizations.

3. Rapid Deployment Capabilities:

Amateur radio operators are trained and equipped to deploy quickly to disaster-affected areas, establishing temporary communication centers, mobile stations, and field operations to support emergency response and recovery efforts.

4. Local and Regional Coverage:

Amateur radio stations, particularly those equipped with low-power or portable equipment, can provide local and regional coverage in areas where traditional communication infrastructure is disrupted or unavailable due to natural disasters, severe weather events, or infrastructure failures.

5. Message Handling and Relay:

Amateur radio operators excel in message handling and relay operations, facilitating the transmission of critical information, requests for assistance, and situational updates between affected areas, emergency operations centers, and relief organizations.

6. Coordination of Resources:

Amateur radio networks facilitate the coordination of resources, assets, and personnel involved in emergency response efforts, enabling effective communication between command centers, field teams, and support agencies.

7. Public Safety Support:

Amateur radio operators provide valuable support to public safety agencies, emergency management authorities, and first responders during emergencies, assisting with communication logistics, resource allocation, and situational awareness.

8. Community Resilience Building:

Amateur radio fosters community resilience by empowering individuals and communities to prepare for, respond to, and recover from emergencies through training, education, and participation in emergency preparedness activities.

9. International Cooperation and Assistance:

Amateur radio operators engage in international cooperation and assistance efforts during large-scale disasters, collaborating with counterparts in other countries to provide mutual aid, information sharing, and technical support.

10. Public Service and Volunteerism:

Amateur radio operators contribute their time, expertise, and resources to public service and volunteer organizations involved in emergency management, disaster response, and community preparedness initiatives.

11. Innovation and Technological Advancement:

Amateur radio fosters innovation and technological advancement in emergency communication systems, encouraging the development of new technologies, protocols, and best practices for resilient and interoperable communication networks.

12. Community Engagement and Outreach:

Amateur radio operators engage in community outreach and education initiatives to raise awareness of the role of amateur radio in emergencies, recruit new operators, and promote the importance of emergency preparedness and resilience.

Amateur radio's role in emergencies underscores its value as a critical communications resource, enabling individuals, communities, and organizations to maintain connectivity, coordinate response efforts, and save lives during times of crisis. As a resilient and adaptable communication platform, amateur radio continues to play an indispensable role in enhancing emergency preparedness and disaster response capabilities worldwide.

7.2 ARES and RACES Organizations

Amateur Radio Emergency Service (ARES) and Radio Amateur Civil Emergency Service (RACES) are two distinct organizations within the amateur radio community dedicated to providing emergency communication support during disasters, crises, and public emergencies. While both ARES and RACES share the common goal of facilitating communication when traditional infrastructure is disrupted, they operate under different auspices and serve distinct roles within the emergency management framework. Here's an overview of ARES and RACES organizations:

1. Amateur Radio Emergency Service (ARES):

ARES is a volunteer organization sponsored by the American Radio Relay League (ARRL) in the United States and affiliated with national and local amateur radio clubs. ARES operators, known as ARES members, are licensed amateur radio operators who volunteer their time, skills, and equipment to support emergency communication efforts in their communities.

ARES members undergo training in emergency communication protocols, procedures, and best practices, preparing them to deploy quickly and effectively during disasters, severe weather events, public safety incidents, and other emergencies.

ARES organizations operate under the guidance and coordination of local emergency management agencies, public safety authorities, and served agencies, collaborating closely with professional responders, government officials, and community stakeholders.

ARES teams establish communication networks, provide tactical and logistical support, relay messages, and assist with coordination and resource allocation during emergency response operations.

ARES emphasizes interoperability, flexibility, and adaptability, working alongside other emergency communication providers, such as RACES, Skywarn spotters, and CERT teams, to enhance overall emergency preparedness and response capabilities.

2. Radio Amateur Civil Emergency Service (RACES):

RACES is a federally authorized emergency communication service administered by the Federal Emergency Management Agency (FEMA) in the United States. RACES operators, known as RACES members, are licensed amateur radio operators who serve as auxiliary communications personnel for civil defense agencies, emergency management offices, and government agencies.

RACES organizations operate under the auspices of state and local emergency management agencies, with members appointed as emergency management volunteers by their respective jurisdictions. RACES members may be activated during declared emergencies or exercises to provide supplemental communication support to government agencies and critical infrastructure providers.

RACES operators receive specialized training in emergency procedures, protocols, and operational requirements specific to their roles as auxiliary communicators supporting civil defense and public safety missions.

RACES communications are conducted using designated frequencies and procedures authorized by FEMA and coordinated with local and state emergency management authorities. RACES operators may be tasked with transmitting essential information, relaying status reports, and facilitating coordination between emergency response agencies during emergencies.

RACES organizations play a vital role in enhancing emergency preparedness, response, and recovery capabilities at the local, state, and federal levels, augmenting existing communication resources and providing a resilient backup communication system when traditional infrastructure is compromised.

While ARES and RACES organizations operate independently and serve different jurisdictions and constituencies, they share a common commitment to public service, emergency preparedness, and the advancement of amateur radio as a vital resource for community resilience and disaster response. By working collaboratively with government agencies, emergency responders, and community stakeholders, ARES and RACES operators contribute their expertise and resources to ensure reliable and effective communication support during times of crisis and uncertainty.

7.3 Training and Preparedness for Public Service Events

Training and preparedness are essential components of amateur radio operators' participation in public service events, such as parades, marathons, and community festivals. These events often require reliable communication support to ensure the safety, coordination, and smooth operation of activities involving large crowds and diverse stakeholders. Amateur radio operators, equipped with their technical skills, communication expertise, and dedication to public service, play a vital role in providing effective communication support during public service events. Here's a guide to training and preparedness for amateur radio operators participating in public service events:

1. Emergency Communication Training:

Obtain training in emergency communication protocols, procedures, and best practices through courses offered by organizations such as the American Radio Relay League (ARRL), Radio Amateur Civil Emergency Service (RACES), and local amateur radio clubs. Familiarize yourself with emergency communication techniques, net operations, message handling, and incident command structures.

2. Public Service Event Orientation:

Attend orientation sessions or briefings conducted by event organizers to familiarize yourself with event logistics, communication requirements, and safety protocols. Obtain information on the event schedule, course routes, staging areas, and designated communication points to facilitate effective communication support.

3. Equipment Preparation:

Prepare and test your amateur radio equipment in advance of the event, ensuring that your transceiver, antenna, power source, and accessories are in good working condition. Pack essential items such as spare batteries, coaxial cables, antennas, and portable antennas for field deployments or mobile operations.

4. Frequency Coordination:

Coordinate frequency usage and operating procedures with other amateur radio operators participating in the event, as well as with event organizers, public safety agencies, and other communication providers. Assign designated frequencies for event communications, including primary, backup, and tactical channels, to avoid interference and ensure efficient communication.

5. Communication Protocols:

Establish communication protocols and procedures for coordinating event activities, reporting incidents, and relaying messages between key personnel, event organizers, and support teams. Use standardized communication formats, such as ICS (Incident

Command System) forms, to facilitate clear and concise message handling.

6. Deployment Planning:

Develop deployment plans and operational strategies for positioning amateur radio operators at strategic locations along the event route or within event venues. Assign roles and responsibilities to operators, including net control, checkpoint monitoring, course marshaling, and emergency response coordination.

7. Safety and Emergency Preparedness:

Prioritize safety and emergency preparedness during public service events, ensuring that operators are equipped with personal protective equipment (PPE), first aid kits, and emergency supplies. Establish procedures for handling medical emergencies, severe weather incidents, and other unforeseen contingencies.

8. Continuous Monitoring and Reporting:

Maintain continuous monitoring of event communications throughout the duration of the event, providing real-time updates, status reports, and incident notifications as necessary. Monitor weather conditions, crowd movements, and potential safety hazards to anticipate and respond to emerging issues promptly.

9. Interagency Collaboration:

Foster collaboration and coordination with event organizers, public safety agencies, emergency responders, and other volunteer groups involved in event management and support. Establish clear lines of communication and mutual aid agreements to facilitate seamless integration of amateur radio resources into the overall event framework.

10. Post-Event Evaluation and Feedback:

Conduct post-event debriefings and evaluations to assess the effectiveness of amateur radio communication support, identify lessons learned, and make recommendations for improvement. Solicit feedback from event organizers, participants, and fellow operators to enhance future preparedness and response efforts.

By investing time and effort in training, preparation, and collaboration, amateur radio operators can enhance their effectiveness and contribution to public service events, ensuring reliable communication support and promoting the safety and success of community gatherings and activities. Embrace the opportunity to serve your community and demonstrate the value of amateur radio as a vital resource for public safety and emergency communication.

CHAPTER 8

8.1 DXing: Chasing Distant Contacts

DXing, or long-distance communication, is a popular pursuit among amateur radio operators who seek to establish contacts with stations located far beyond their local or regional vicinity. DXing presents a rewarding challenge that requires skill, patience, and technical expertise, as operators endeavor to overcome geographical barriers, atmospheric conditions, and propagation challenges to reach distant locations around the globe. Here's a comprehensive guide to DXing and chasing distant contacts in amateur radio:

1. Understanding DXing:

DXing refers to the practice of making contacts with amateur radio stations located in distant or "DX" locations, typically beyond one's own country or continent. DXing enthusiasts strive to communicate with rare, exotic, or sought-after locations, often collecting confirmations or "QSL cards" as proof of successful contacts.

2. Research and Propagation Prediction:

Conduct research and utilize propagation prediction tools to identify optimal times, frequencies, and propagation modes for contacting DX stations. Monitor solar activity, ionospheric conditions, and geomagnetic disturbances to anticipate favorable propagation windows and maximize your chances of success.

3. Operating Technique:

Employ effective operating techniques and strategies to enhance your chances of making DX contacts. Use directional antennas, low-angle radiation patterns, and beam steering to target specific geographic regions or azimuths where DX stations are likely to be located. Listen attentively, practice good frequency etiquette, and follow established DXing protocols to optimize your operating efficiency.

4. DXpeditions and Special Events:

Participate in DXpeditions, special events, and contests dedicated to DXing to increase your opportunities for making rare or exotic contacts. Join organized expeditions to remote or uninhabited locations, or participate in contests that attract DX operators from around the world, providing a concentrated opportunity for DXing activity.

5. Operating Modes and Bands:

Experiment with different operating modes and frequency bands to maximize your DXing capabilities. Utilize high-frequency (HF) bands such as 20 meters, 15 meters, and 10 meters for long-distance communication, as well as lower-frequency bands during periods of enhanced propagation conditions, such as 160 meters and 80 meters.

6. Antenna and Equipment Optimization:

Invest in high-performance antennas, amplifiers, and receivers optimized for DXing to improve your station's signal strength, sensitivity, and directional capabilities. Fine-tune antenna installations, antenna matching networks, and transmission line configurations to minimize losses and maximize radiated power.

7. Persistence and Patience:

Exercise persistence and patience when DXing, as successful contacts with distant stations may require repeated attempts, careful timing, and adaptation to changing propagation conditions. Maintain a vigilant watch for openings in propagation, and be prepared to seize opportunities for contacting DX stations when conditions are favorable.

8. QSLing and Confirmation:

Exchange QSL cards or electronic confirmations with DX stations as proof of your contact, demonstrating mutual respect and appreciation for successful communication. Follow established QSLing procedures, including sending cards promptly, accurately, and via preferred delivery methods specified by the DX station.

9. Log Keeping and Documentation:

Maintain detailed logs of your DXing activities, including date, time, frequency, mode, signal reports, and station details for each contact made. Use logging software or paper logs to record essential information accurately, enabling you to track your DXing achievements and progress over time.

10. Enjoy the Journey:

Embrace the adventure and excitement of DXing, appreciating the diversity of cultures, landscapes, and experiences encountered through amateur radio contacts with stations around the world. Celebrate each successful DX contact as a testament to your skill, perseverance, and passion for the hobby.

By immersing yourself in the art and science of DXing, you can embark on a rewarding journey of exploration, discovery, and camaraderie, connecting with fellow amateur radio enthusiasts across continents and oceans while pushing the boundaries of communication and technology. Whether you're chasing rare entities, collecting awards, or simply enjoying the thrill of making distant contacts, DXing offers endless opportunities for adventure and fulfillment in the world of amateur radio.

8.2 Contesting: Competing in On-Air Events

Contesting is a thrilling aspect of amateur radio that allows operators to compete in on-air events, testing their skills, equipment, and operating prowess against fellow enthusiasts worldwide. Amateur radio contests offer a platform for operators to showcase their proficiency in making contacts, maximizing their station's performance, and accumulating points or scores based on predefined rules and criteria. Whether you're a seasoned contester or a newcomer to the hobby, participating in contests provides an exciting opportunity to engage in friendly competition, hone your operating skills, and connect with fellow radio amateurs. Here's a comprehensive guide to contesting in amateur radio:

1. Understanding Contesting:

Contesting involves participating in organized on-air events where amateur radio operators compete to make the most contacts with other stations within a specified time frame, frequency band, or operating mode. Contests may focus on specific bands, modes (e.g., CW, SSB, digital), or themes, such as DXing, field operations, or low-power operation.

2. Contest Categories:

Contests offer a variety of categories to accommodate operators of different experience levels, station setups, and operating preferences. Categories may include single-operator, multi-operator, or team entries, as well as classifications based on power output, antenna restrictions, geographical location, and license class.

3. Contest Preparation:

Prepare your station and equipment for contest operation by ensuring that all components are in optimal working condition. Test antennas, transceivers, amplifiers, and accessories to verify performance and reliability, and address any technical issues or deficiencies before the contest begins.

4. Contest Strategy:

Develop a contest strategy based on the contest rules, operating conditions, and your personal objectives. Determine your target operating bands, modes, and operating times, taking into account propagation conditions, band openings, and anticipated rates of activity to maximize your scoring potential.

5. Operating Techniques:

Employ effective operating techniques to maximize your contact rate and score during the contest. Use efficient calling and logging procedures, such as tail-ending, frequency spotting, and keyboard shortcuts, to expedite contact exchanges and minimize downtime between QSOs.

6. Logging and Dupe Checking:

Maintain accurate logs of all contest contacts, recording essential information such as call signs, exchange information, time, frequency, and mode for each QSO. Use contest logging software or paper logs to facilitate rapid data entry, dupe checking, and scoring validation during and after the contest.

7. Frequency Management:

Manage your operating frequency and bandwidth responsibly, avoiding interference with other contest participants, ongoing conversations, or net operations on adjacent frequencies. Monitor band plans, DX clusters, and contest spotting networks to identify available frequencies and minimize conflicts with other stations.

8. Pacing and Endurance:

Pace yourself and maintain endurance throughout the contest, balancing operating intensity with rest periods and breaks to sustain your focus and energy levels. Stay hydrated, take short breaks for meals and relaxation, and avoid fatigue-induced errors or burnout during extended operating sessions.

9. Sportsmanship and Fair Play:

Conduct yourself with sportsmanship and fair play throughout the contest, adhering to contest rules, ethical standards, and operating guidelines established by contest sponsors and organizing bodies. Treat fellow contestants with respect, refrain from unsportsmanlike conduct, and resolve disputes or conflicts amicably.

10. Post-Contest Analysis:

Perform a post-contest analysis of your performance, reviewing your logs, scores, and operating techniques to identify strengths, weaknesses, and areas for improvement. Evaluate your contest strategy, equipment setup, and operating tactics to refine your approach and enhance your competitive edge in future contests.

11. Awards and Recognition:

Celebrate your contest achievements and accomplishments, whether through personal milestones, category wins, or participation in team efforts. Collect awards, certificates, and accolades from contest sponsors and organizing bodies, recognizing your contributions to the amateur radio contesting community.

12. Enjoy the Experience:

Above all, enjoy the experience of contesting and the camaraderie of participating in on-air events with fellow radio amateurs around the world. Embrace the excitement, challenges, and sense of achievement that come with contesting, and relish the opportunity to showcase your skills and passion for amateur radio.

By immersing yourself in the world of amateur radio contesting, you can embark on a thrilling journey of competition, camaraderie, and personal growth, pushing the limits of your operating abilities while forging lasting connections with fellow enthusiasts worldwide. Whether you're vying for top honors, pursuing personal goals, or simply enjoying the thrill of the chase, contesting offers an exhilarating and rewarding pursuit within the vibrant tapestry of amateur radio.

Experimenting with homebrew equipment is a rewarding aspect of amateur radio that allows operators to explore their creativity, technical skills, and ingenuity by designing, building, and testing their own radio equipment and accessories. Homebrewing offers a hands-on approach to amateur radio, enabling operators to customize their setups, learn about radio theory, and gain a deeper understanding of the principles underlying radio communication. Whether you're a novice builder or a seasoned experimenter, homebrewing provides endless opportunities for innovation, learning, and enjoyment in the amateur radio hobby. Here's a comprehensive guide to experimenting with homebrew equipment:

1. Understanding Homebrewing:

Homebrewing involves the construction, modification, or customization of radio equipment, antennas, accessories, and components using DIY (do-it-yourself) methods and techniques. Homebrewers often design and build their projects from scratch, using schematics, plans, or improvisation to create unique and personalized solutions tailored to their needs.

2. Choosing Projects:

Select homebrew projects that align with your interests, skills, and goals in amateur radio. Consider projects that match your proficiency level, available resources, and equipment capabilities, whether you're interested in building simple kits, modifying commercial gear, or designing advanced circuits from scratch.

3. Learning Resources:

Take advantage of educational resources, instructional materials, and online communities dedicated to homebrewing in amateur radio. Explore books, manuals, websites, and forums that offer guidance, tutorials, and project ideas for aspiring homebrewers, covering topics such as circuit design, construction techniques, and troubleshooting tips.

4. Starting Simple:

Begin with simple and straightforward projects to build confidence and foundational skills in homebrewing. Start with basic kits, circuits, or modules that require minimal components and construction techniques, such as antenna tuners, keyers, or power supplies, before progressing to more complex projects.

5. Acquiring Tools and Equipment:

Acquire the necessary tools, equipment, and supplies for homebrewing, including soldering irons, multimeters, oscilloscopes, hand tools, and electronic components. Invest in quality tools suited to your projects and workspace, ensuring safety, precision, and reliability throughout the construction process.

6. Experimentation and Innovation:

Embrace experimentation and innovation in your homebrewing endeavors, exploring new ideas, techniques, and configurations to push the boundaries of amateur radio technology. Experiment with different circuit topologies, component values, and construction methods to achieve desired performance characteristics and functionality.

7. Testing and Evaluation:

Test and evaluate your homebrew projects systematically to assess their performance, reliability, and compatibility with your operating requirements.

Conduct bench tests, on-air trials, and field evaluations to validate functionality, measure performance metrics, and identify areas for improvement or optimization.

8. Documentation and Sharing:

Document your homebrew projects thoroughly, keeping detailed records of circuit diagrams, parts lists, assembly instructions, and performance data for future reference and replication. Share your experiences, insights, and project outcomes with fellow homebrewers, amateur radio clubs, and online communities to inspire others and contribute to the collective knowledge base.

9. Iterative Improvement:

Embrace an iterative approach to homebrewing, continuously refining and improving your projects based on feedback, experimentation, and lessons learned from previous iterations. Iterate on design iterations, incorporate user feedback, and explore alternative solutions to enhance functionality, reliability, and user experience.

10. Safety and Compliance:

Prioritize safety and compliance in all aspects of homebrewing, adhering to best practices, safety guidelines, and regulatory requirements governing the construction, operation, and testing of amateur radio equipment. Follow established safety protocols, handle electronic components responsibly, and observe electrical safety precautions to minimize risks of injury or damage.

By immersing yourself in the world of homebrewing, you can unleash your creativity, expand your technical skills, and deepen your appreciation for the art and science of amateur radio. Whether you're building your first project or tackling advanced designs, homebrewing provides a fulfilling and enriching experience that fosters lifelong learning, personal growth, and connection within the amateur radio community.

CHAPTER 9

CONNECTING WITH THE HAM RADIO COMMUNITY

9.1 Joining Clubs and Organizations

Joining clubs and organizations is an excellent way for amateur radio operators to connect with like-minded enthusiasts, participate in community activities, and gain access to valuable resources, support, and opportunities for learning and collaboration. Amateur radio clubs and organizations provide a vibrant and inclusive community where operators can share their passion for the hobby, exchange knowledge and experiences, and contribute to the advancement of amateur radio. Whether you're a newcomer seeking guidance or an experienced operator looking to expand your network, joining clubs and organizations offers numerous benefits and enriching experiences. Here's a comprehensive guide to joining clubs and organizations in the amateur radio community:

1. Identifying Local Clubs:

Research and identify amateur radio clubs and organizations in your local area, region, or community.

Explore online directories, club listings, and social media platforms to discover clubs that align with your interests, geographical proximity, and operating preferences.

2. Attending Club Meetings:

Attend club meetings, gatherings, or events to meet fellow operators, learn about club activities, and get a sense of the club's culture, mission, and values. Participate in club meetings, presentations, and activities to engage with members, share your interests, and contribute to club initiatives.

3. Participating in Club Activities:

Participate actively in club activities, projects, and events that align with your interests and goals in amateur radio. Join in on field days, contests, antenna-building workshops, public service events, and educational programs organized by the club to expand your skills, network with peers, and contribute to the amateur radio community.

4. Contributing to Club Projects:

Contribute your expertise, resources, and enthusiasm to club projects, initiatives, and committees focused on amateur radio promotion, education, public service, and technical innovation. Volunteer for leadership roles, event coordination, or mentoring opportunities to make a meaningful impact within the club and the broader amateur radio community.

5. Engaging Online Communities:

Engage with online communities, forums, and social media groups dedicated to amateur radio clubs and organizations. Connect with fellow operators, share experiences, seek advice, and stay informed about club activities, announcements, and discussions happening in virtual spaces.

6. Joining National and International Organizations:

Consider joining national and international amateur radio organizations, such as the American Radio Relay League (ARRL), Radio Society of Great Britain (RSGB), or International Amateur Radio Union (IARU), to access a wide range of resources, benefits, and services tailored to amateur radio enthusiasts worldwide.

7. Subscribing to Publications and Newsletters:

Subscribe to club publications, newsletters, and mailing lists to stay informed about club news, upcoming events, technical articles, and member achievements. Stay connected with the club community, receive updates on club activities, and access valuable educational and informational resources.

8. Building Relationships and Networks:

Build relationships and networks with fellow club members, mentors, and industry professionals within the amateur radio community. Foster friendships, mentorship opportunities, and collaborative partnerships that enrich your amateur radio experience and support your personal and professional growth as an operator.

9. Exploring Special Interest Groups:

Explore special interest groups, sub-clubs, or focus areas within larger amateur radio organizations that cater to specific interests, modes, activities, or technical specialties. Join SIGs dedicated to DXing, contesting, digital modes, satellite operations, emergency communication, or youth outreach to connect with enthusiasts who share your passions and expertise.

10. Contributing to the Community:

Contribute to the amateur radio community by sharing your knowledge, experiences, and resources with fellow operators, newcomers, and aspiring enthusiasts. Mentor newcomers, teach licensing classes, participate in outreach programs, or volunteer for public service events to give back to the hobby and inspire others to pursue their interests in amateur radio.

By joining clubs and organizations in the amateur radio community, you can immerse yourself in a supportive and collaborative environment that celebrates the diversity, creativity, and camaraderie of amateur radio enthusiasts worldwide. Whether you're seeking camaraderie, mentorship, learning opportunities, or avenues for personal growth, clubs and organizations offer a welcoming and enriching space where operators of all backgrounds and skill levels can thrive and contribute to the vibrancy and vitality of the amateur radio hobby.

Participating in nets and roundtables is an integral aspect of amateur radio that allows operators to engage in structured on-air gatherings, exchange information, and foster camaraderie within the amateur radio community. Nets and roundtables provide opportunities for operators to connect with fellow enthusiasts, share experiences, and discuss topics of mutual interest while practicing effective communication skills and protocol adherence. Whether you're a seasoned operator or a newcomer to the hobby, participating in nets and roundtables offers valuable experiences, learning opportunities, and social interactions. Here's a comprehensive guide to participating in nets and roundtables in amateur radio:

1. Understanding Nets:

Nets are scheduled on-air meetings or gatherings of amateur radio operators organized around a specific purpose, theme, or topic of discussion. Nets may serve various purposes, including emergency communication, traffic handling, public service coordination, training, social interaction, or technical discussions.

2. Identifying Net Types:

Explore different types of nets based on their objectives, formats, and operating protocols. Common types of nets include directed nets, where a net control station (NCS) manages traffic flow and discussions, informal nets, where participants engage in casual conversation and socializing, and formal nets, where operators follow specific procedures and protocols.

3. Finding Nets to Join:

Find nets to join by consulting online directories, club newsletters, repeater directories, and social media groups that list scheduled nets and roundtables. Explore nets that align with your interests, operating preferences, and availability, and consider joining local, regional, or specialized nets focused on topics such as emergency preparedness, DXing, or technical discussions.

4. Following Net Protocols:

Follow established net protocols, procedures, and etiquette when participating in nets and roundtables.

Listen carefully to net control instructions, wait for your turn to speak, and adhere to established operating practices, such as using clear phonetics, identifying your call sign, and waiting for acknowledgment before transmitting.

5. Contributing to Discussions:

Contribute actively to discussions during nets and roundtables by sharing relevant information, experiences, and insights on the designated topic or theme. Listen attentively to other participants, show respect for diverse viewpoints, and avoid dominating the conversation to ensure equitable participation and engagement among all participants.

6. Offering Assistance and Support:

Offer assistance and support to fellow operators during nets and roundtables, especially in situations where help is needed, questions arise, or technical issues occur. Provide guidance, resources, and encouragement to newcomers, less experienced operators, or those seeking assistance with equipment, operating techniques, or amateur radio topics.

7. Building Relationships:

Build relationships and connections with fellow net participants by engaging in meaningful conversations, sharing common interests, and fostering camaraderie within the amateur radio community. Establish rapport, exchange contact information, and follow up with fellow operators outside of nets to nurture ongoing friendships and collaborations.

8. Practicing Good Operating Habits:

Practice good operating habits and communication skills during nets and roundtables, including clear and concise speech, courteous behavior, and adherence to net procedures and guidelines. Demonstrate professionalism, patience, and respect for net control and fellow participants to promote a positive and constructive atmosphere within the net.

9. Seeking Learning Opportunities:

Seek learning opportunities and educational experiences during nets and roundtables by listening to discussions, asking questions, and seeking clarification on topics of interest. Take advantage of the collective knowledge and expertise of net participants to expand your understanding of amateur radio concepts, practices, and techniques.

10. Enjoying Social Interaction:

Enjoy the social interaction and camaraderie of participating in nets and roundtables, connecting with fellow enthusiasts, and building friendships within the amateur radio community. Embrace the opportunity to share experiences, stories, and laughter while fostering a sense of belonging and community spirit among net participants.

By actively participating in nets and roundtables, amateur radio operators can enhance their communication skills, expand their knowledge base, and cultivate meaningful relationships within the amateur radio community. Whether you're seeking information, camaraderie, or simply enjoying casual conversation, nets and roundtables offer a welcoming and inclusive environment where operators of all backgrounds and experience levels can come together to connect, learn, and share their passion for amateur radio.

Attending hamfests and conventions is an exciting and enriching experience for amateur radio enthusiasts, providing opportunities to explore the latest equipment, technologies, and trends in the hobby, meet fellow operators, and participate in educational seminars, workshops, and social activities. Hamfests and conventions serve as gathering points for the amateur radio community, offering a vibrant and dynamic environment where operators can learn, network, and celebrate their shared passion for radio communication. Whether you're a seasoned operator or a newcomer to the hobby, attending hamfests and conventions offers a host of benefits and rewarding experiences. Here's a comprehensive guide to attending hamfests and conventions in the amateur radio community:

1. Understanding Hamfests:

Hamfests are gatherings, events, or conventions organized by amateur radio clubs, organizations, or enthusiasts to bring together operators, vendors, and exhibitors for the purpose of buying, selling, trading, and showcasing amateur radio equipment, accessories, and services. Hamfests may feature flea markets, equipment demonstrations, antenna displays, and educational activities.

2. Identifying Conventions:

Conventions are larger-scale events, conferences, or gatherings that attract amateur radio enthusiasts from a broader geographic region or national/international audience. Conventions typically feature keynote speakers, panel discussions, technical presentations, vendor exhibits, and social events tailored to the interests and needs of attendees.

3. Finding Events to Attend:

Find hamfests and conventions to attend by consulting event calendars, club newsletters, online forums, and social media groups dedicated to amateur radio. Explore regional, national, and international events that align with your interests, availability, and travel preferences, and mark your calendar for upcoming gatherings.

4. Exploring Vendor Exhibits:

Explore vendor exhibits and commercial displays at hamfests and conventions to discover the latest amateur radio equipment, accessories, and technologies available on the market. Visit vendor booths, interact with representatives, and compare products, prices, and features to make informed purchasing decisions and stay abreast of industry trends.

5. Participating in Flea Markets:

Participate in flea markets and swap meets at hamfests to buy, sell, or trade amateur radio equipment, parts, and accessories with fellow operators. Browse through tables, bins, and displays showcasing a diverse array of used, vintage, and surplus radio gear, antennas, components, and collectibles.

6. Attending Educational Sessions:

Attend educational sessions, seminars, and workshops offered at hamfests and conventions to expand your knowledge, skills, and expertise in amateur radio. Learn from expert presenters, industry professionals, and fellow enthusiasts who share insights, tips, and best practices on a wide range of topics, including antenna design, propagation, digital modes, contesting, emergency communication, and more.

7. Networking and Socializing:

Network with fellow operators, enthusiasts, and industry representatives during hamfests and conventions, fostering new friendships, professional connections, and collaborative partnerships within the amateur radio community. Engage in casual conversations, share experiences, and exchange contact information to stay connected beyond the event.

8. Participating in Special Events:

Participate in special events, activities, and demonstrations organized as part of hamfests and conventions, such as antenna-building workshops, kit-building sessions, fox hunts, license testing sessions, and on-air demonstrations. Get hands-on experience, learn new skills, and immerse yourself in the excitement and camaraderie of amateur radio.

9. Supporting Amateur Radio Organizations:

Support amateur radio clubs, organizations, and associations that host hamfests and conventions by attending their events, volunteering your time and expertise, and becoming a member or supporter. Contribute to the success and sustainability of amateur radio activities, initiatives, and community-building efforts through active participation and engagement.

10. Enjoying the Experience:

Above all, enjoy the experience of attending hamfests and conventions, immersing yourself in the vibrant and dynamic atmosphere of the amateur radio community. Embrace the opportunity to connect with fellow enthusiasts, explore new interests, and celebrate the shared passion for radio communication that unites operators around the world.

By attending hamfests and conventions, amateur radio operators can expand their horizons, enhance their skills, and forge lasting connections within the vibrant and diverse amateur radio community. Whether you're seeking equipment upgrades, educational opportunities, or social interaction, hamfests and conventions offer a welcoming and inclusive environment where operators of all backgrounds and interests can come together to celebrate their shared love of radio communication.

CONCLUSION

The world of amateur radio offers a rich tapestry of experiences, opportunities, and camaraderie for enthusiasts of all backgrounds and interests. From the foundational principles of radio communication to the thrill of chasing distant contacts and the camaraderie of participating in nets and roundtables, amateur radio provides a gateway to exploration, learning, and community engagement. Whether you're delving into the basics of ham radio operation, building your own equipment through homebrewing, or participating in contests, public service events, or emergency communication initiatives, amateur radio offers endless avenues for personal growth, technical discovery, and social interaction.

By joining clubs and organizations, attending hamfests and conventions, and participating in on-air activities, operators can connect with fellow enthusiasts, share knowledge and experiences, and contribute to the vibrancy and resilience of the amateur radio community. Through collaboration, education, and advocacy, amateur radio operators play a vital role in promoting the values of innovation, service, and fellowship that define the amateur radio hobby.

As we continue to embrace the challenges and opportunities of the digital age, the enduring appeal of amateur radio persists, serving as a beacon of exploration, innovation, and connection in an ever-changing world. Whether you're an experienced operator or a newcomer to the hobby, the adventure of amateur radio awaits, inviting you to embark on a journey of discovery, friendship, and lifelong learning in the fascinating realm of radio communication.

Made in United States
North Haven, CT
28 September 2024